Kevon's Big Field Day

We Should All Have A Chance

Written by **Kevon Lee**

Illustrated by **Viona Betzy**

This Book Belongs to:

_____

Motivation only gets us so far.
Let's empower ourselves and those around us.

"Today is field day, and I'm afraid I will either lose or not play well."

"Well I know you'll do a great job.
Now come on, let's get in the car."

Kevon sighs "Grandma, what if I don't win any of the games? What if the other kids laugh at me?"

"You can't think that way. The other kids will be nervous too. Your thoughts are very powerful. Think positively and believe in yourself."

"I don't want to look bad in front of my friends. I don't want to lose."

"You're a winner, no matter if you win or lose. It's about showing up, doing your very best, and having fun."

"Tell yourself that you're a winner instead of worrying about losing. Now go on and have some fun!"

Lesson 1 : The words we tell ourselves are powerful. So, focus on the positive and limit your negative thoughts.

"I'm so nervous about field day. But I'm going to listen to my grandma and try to have fun. But first, I must find my friends."

"Hey, Luis!"
Kevon shouts and runs
towards the sack race.

"I'll race with you. I'm nervous too, but my grandma said it's important just to have fun. So let's have fun!"

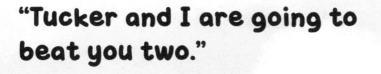

"Tucker and I are going to beat you two."

"That's okay, Anaya. Luis and I are just having fun. But, bring it on anyway!"

START

"I'm right behind you, Kevon," Anaya says.
"I thought you were going to win, Anaya?!"

Lesson 2: We only lose if we don't try. In life, we must face every obstacle, no matter how big or small. We can only achieve our best if we put in the effort.

"Yay! Kevon," Luis says.
"I got second place! That was so much fun.
Congratulations on winning, Anaya."

"Thank you! Racing you was so much fun.
Congratulations to you too."

I'm so sorry I tripped. We're going to lose, and it's my fault. Please do not be mad at me."

"Let me help you up. I'm not mad but come on, we can still finish this race! No matter what place we get, it's important that we finish."

"Thank you for inspiring me, Kevon."
"What are friends for?"

Lesson 3: We need to surround ourselves with people who see the best in us and are willing to help us express it.

"I'm joking, Tucker. All that matters,
is that we're having fun."

As the horn sounds, Kevon and Tucker take off.
Tucker takes the lead.

"Here's your first place ribbon Kevon! Great job! You should be very proud of yourself."

"Thank you, Mr. English!"

"Hey Tucker, don't be sad. You gave it your best. We had fun and you didn't give up. We're both winners."

"Are you sure you want me to have your first place ribbon?"

"Making a friend feel better is more important to me than winning."

Lesson 4: Winning is not about ribbons. It's about how you encourage and impact those around you on your way to

"How was your field day, Kevon?"

"It was great. I lost some games and won some other games. You were right, I had to think positively and believe in myself. I had fun. Thank you, grandma. I love you."

"I love you more, Kevon."

Kevon's Big Field Day
We Should all Have a Chance
Copyright© 2021 by IMPACTpublishing, Inc.

www.ImpactPublishing.Ink

Printed in the United States.

First Edition, 2021

ISBN: 9781955509015

Impact Publishing, Inc.
P.O. Box 27311
San Antonio, TX 78227

Graphic Design by: Viona Betzy
Formatted by: Indalecio Chavez, Jr.

CPSIA information can be obtained
at www.ICGtesting.com
Printed in the USA
LVHW050951120222
710938LV00004B/11

9 781955 509015